C000059536

AN AVIAN ALPHABET

AN
AVIAN
ALPHABET

WRITTEN AND ILLUSTRATED BY

MAGGIE DIMON

O'LEARY
PUBLISHING
The Influencer's Press

NAPLES, FL

ISBN: 978-1-952491-56-6
Library of Congress Control Number: 2023907866

Proofreading by Kat Langenheim
Cover and interior design layout by Jessica Angerstein

Printed in the United States of America

Pay attention.
Be astonished.
Tell about it.

~Mary Oliver
from "Sometimes"

CONTENTS

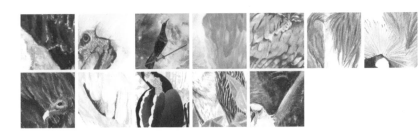

INTRODUCTION

It all started when I found an abandoned baby Green Heron.
I wrapped him in a towel, put him in a box, and carried him
to the von Arx Wildlife Hospital here in Naples, Florida. After
the staff nursed him for eleven days, I was privileged to see a
beautiful, healthy bird released back into his natural habitat.

Since then, I have been enamored of birds and their diversity
of color, size, song, and behavior. I study birds, create images
of birds, write about birds, and care for birds at the Wildlife
Hospital where I now volunteer.

I didn't set out to write a book, but one thing led to another. At some point I had so many drawings, I realized I was well on my way to creating an image for every letter of the alphabet. The alphabet complete, my writing partner encouraged me to write a poem for each of the birds. I followed the music.

I have always been an artist and a writer, but this is the first time I've combined these loves. Putting my work into book form and sending it out into the world gives it wings and song. Please join me in the chorus with our avian friends and let the music carry you to new places.

Anhinga

The snake-bird's neck becomes an S.
Watch out! His bill's a spear!
He dives below to dine on fish
Then spreads his wings to air.

BLUE HERON

Majestic bird, a sentinel
In reeds beside the bay.
We tread too close, he startles –
On wide wings glides away.

Cormorant

When Cormorant wants to woo a mate
He gussies up with bling.
A jeweled eye and orange face
Are his engagement ring.

Duck

Mottled Ducks* flock to our pond,
Yet elsewhere they are rare.
These dabbling ducks could soon be gone.
Admire them while they're here!

*The Mottled Duck is on the Red Watch List of Partners in Flight (PIF),
the highest level of conservation concern.*

Egret

Like a bride arranging her train
While she awaits her groom,
Elegance is the Great Egret
Preening her ivory plumes.

Frigatebird

Frigatebird with wings spread wide

Flies high above the sea,

Soars spirals in the vast blue sky,

Magnificent is he!

Green Heron

His chestnut-colored neck pulled close
Against his shining blue green back.
Stock-still he holds a focused crouch
And waits to launch his brisk attack.

hooded merganser

This little duck's a thrill to see –
He flaunts his round white hood,
Then vanishes with sudden dive
To the depths to hunt for food.

Ibis

Whoosh of wings at end of day –
Flocks fly over to roost.
White Ibises of Rookery Bay
Gather in the mangroves.

jay

The Florida scrub is this Jay's niche,
His habitat is rare.
The Oaks provide him with his cache –
Eight thousand acorns a year!

Kestrel

He claims his perch with tail a-bob
And calls out Klee! Klee! Klee!
Our smallest falcon hunts for bugs
From high up in his tree.

Loggerhead Shrike

Shrike strikes.
Black-masked bandit
Impales
Insects, lizards.
Fills his pantry
To prove his prowess.

Mockingbird

Mockingbird is feathered song,
Two hundred tunes learns he.
Whistling, trilling all day long
For joy and mastery.

NIGHTJAR

This night-flyer hunts at dusk and dawn
Or by the full moon's light.
Mouth agape in giant yawn –
Traps beetles, moths in flight.

osprey

Osprey hovers over waves,
Her hawk-eye focused on the surf,
Then dives feet-first to snag her prey
Sharp talons clutch a startled fish.

Pelican

Pelican's headshot tells his story.

Brown neck: First-year bird.

Grey neck: Second-year bird.

White neck with brown stripe:
Adult bird in summer.

White neck with yellow head:
Adult bird in winter.

White neck, brown stripe, yellow head:
One month of spring fever!

Quiscalus Major Boat-tailed Grackle

His feathered coat's a starry night
Of iridescent hues.
Can you see the universe
In Boat-tailed Grackle's plumes?

Roseate Spoonbill

Roseates forage in a group
For meals of crab and shrimp.
Crustaceans caught with spoon-billed scoop
Keep their feathers pink.

SCREECH OWL

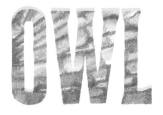

This tiny owl with tufted ears
Hunts silently at night.
The sun comes up – he disappears
By hiding in plain sight.

Tricolored Heron

Feathered in purple, white and blue
As his name "Tricolored" implies,
This Heron's adorned in a rainbow of hues,
Pink legs, buff plumes, red eyes.

UGANDA'S NATIONAL BIRD

The Crested Cranes with golden crowns
Are famous for their dance –
Jumping up and bowing down,
Wings flaring while they prance.

Vulture

Be grateful for the clean-up crew
As Vultures feast on carrion,
Performing service no other can do –
They curb the spread of bacteria.

WOOD STORK

Bald-headed stork with gnarly neck,
Up close a wizened sight –
Wings spread wide, he steals my breath,
Inspires awe in flight.

eXtinct?

Ghost Bird

Lost Bird

Lord God Bird.

Extinct?

Or alive

In the Bayou DeView

Or the Fakahatchee Strand?

Ivory-billed Woodpecker

Was

Or Is?

YELLOW-CROWNED NIGHT HERON

Solitary heron
Hides in the mangroves
By the Gordon River.
Avian of the night,
I know where to find you,
Wading in the shallows
Even in the daytime
If the tide is right.

*The African Fish Eagle, a symbol of strength, is the national bird
of Zambia, Zimbabwe, Malawi, and South Sudan.

Zambia's national bird
african
fish eagle*

Perched high above a clean, clear lake
The eagle gives his catch a shake,
Then calls, triumphant, to his mate.

ARTIST'S MEDIUMS

Anhinga – Paper collage with feather
Blue Heron – Colored pencil
Cormorant – Magazine and found-paper collage
Duck – Colored pencil
Egret – Colored pencil
Frigatebird – Magazine and found-paper collage
Green Heron – Colored pencil
Hooded Merganser – Mosaic of cut paint-swatches
Ibis – Mosaic of cut paint-swatches
Jay – Colored pencil
Kestrel – Found-paper collage
Loggerhead Shrike – Found-paper collage
Mockingbird – Collage made from pages of old sheet music
Nightjar – Colored pencil
Osprey – Oil pastel
Pelican – Colored pencil
Quiscalus Major – Collage from images of the universe
Roseate Spoonbill – Colored pencil
Screech Owl – Colored pencil
Tricolored Heron – Colored pencil
Uganda's national bird – Colored pencil
Vulture – Oil pastels
Wood Stork – Colored pencil
X (Ivory-billed Woodpecker) – Paper collage
Yellow-crowned Night Heron – Colored pencil
Zambia's national bird – Colored pencil

ACKNOWLEDGMENTS

A deep thank you to

Professor Roger Bailey who told me
"The art world needs you."

Virginia DuPre whose Atlanta studio and
garden invited me into child-like play.

Natalie Goldberg for her New Mexico writing retreats.

Mary Cumming for always gathering writers at her
table. Thank you, Mary, for your unwavering friendship.

ABOUT THE AUTHOR

Maggie Dimon is an artist and nature enthusiast currently residing in Naples, Florida. Her volunteer work at the von Arx Wildlife Hospital at the Conservancy of Southwest Florida brings her into close contact with native wildlife. Maggie is a dedicated yogi who also enjoys traveling with her husband to visit far-flung family throughout the United States and Africa.

Ingram Content Group UK Ltd.
Milton Keynes UK
UKHW050349210623
423785UK00002B/3